The Hare and the Tortoise

A play by Julia Donaldson
Illustrated by Binny Talib

Characters

Cow

Sheep

Dog

Hare

Hen

Tortoise

3

Dog: See that hare?

Sheep: What hare where?

Hare: This hare here!

Cow: That hare there!

Hen: Watch him run and hop and leap.

Tortoise: Does he ever go to sleep?

Hare: How about a race? Let's see **who** can run as fast as me!

Dog: Race with you?

Hen: You must be crazy.

Sheep: I'm too slow.

Cow: And I'm too lazy.

Tortoise: Maybe I could have a go?

Dog: Tortoise?

Sheep: TORTOISE?

Cow: He's so slow.

Hare: Ha ha ha! Hee hee hee!

Come on, Tortoise!
Race with me!

Down the hill, then
through the wood.

Then back again?

Tortoise: Yes, that sounds good.

Hare: All sit down and
watch me win.

Cow: Are you ready?

Hen: Let's begin.

Start/Finish

Tortoise

Har

Dog: One, two, three, and OFF YOU GO!

Sheep: Poor old Tortoise. He's so slow.

Tortoise: Slow and steady! Slow and steady!

Sheep: Hare is down the hill already.

8

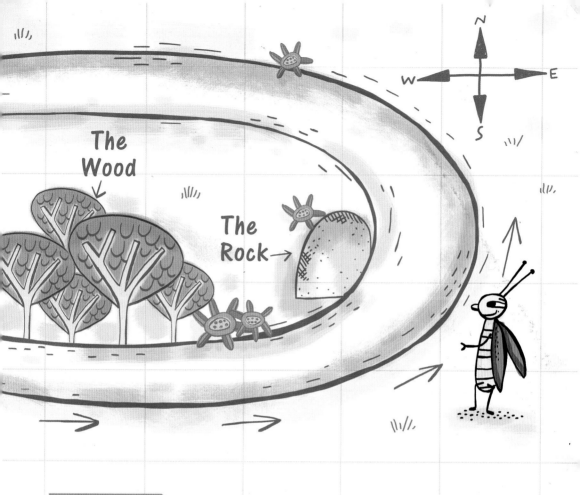

Cow:	Now he's run into the wood.
Dog:	Poor old Tortoise. He's no good.
Hen:	Hare is out the other side!
Sheep:	Poor old Tortoise!
Cow:	Well, he tried.

Tortoise: Keep on going.
Keep on going.

Dog: Here comes Hare.

Hen: But look, he's slowing.

Tortoise: One foot, two feet,
three feet, four.

Hare: This is easy! What a bore!

Sheep: Hare is yawning.

Cow: Hare is stopping.

Dog: Look at him!
His ears are flopping.

Hare: I think I'll have a little nap
before I run the final lap.

11

Sheep: Hare is yawning!

Cow: Hare is sleeping!

Tortoise: Keep on creeping.
Keep on creeping.

Dog: Hare, wake up!

Sheep: No, let's not wake him.

Cow: Let's watch Tortoise
overtake him!

Hen: Good old Tortoise keeps on going.

Sheep: Never stopping.

Cow: Never slowing.

Hen: Hare has been asleep all morning!

Dog: Now he's waking, stretching, yawning.

Hare: Where's that tortoise? Never mind.

I must have left him far behind.

Dog: Look, Hare, look! Don't sit there grinning.

Look ahead and see who's winning!

14

Sheep: Tortoise is ahead of you!

Hare: Tortoise? No,
it can't be true!

Cow: Yes it is!

Hare: Well, goodness me!
I'll soon catch up, though
– wait and see.

Tortoise: Keep on creeping.
Keep on creeping.

Hen: Hare is hopping.

Sheep: Hare is leaping.

Cow: Can he do it?

Dog: Run, Hare, run!

Sheep: It's too late.
Just look who's won!

Cow: Poor old Hare!
Just see his face!

Hen: Good old Tortoise
wins the race.